D1538757

EMOTES!®

THE CREATION

When the emotions of all Internet users came together, a new super-energy was created. This energy split into unique beings, each of which represents a different emotion. They are the Emotes!

A-NET
(THE MENTOR)

SUPER
(THE CONFIDENT)

JOI
(THE EXCITED)

ABASH
(THE EMBARRASSED)

YAWNI
(THE BORED)

ICK
(THE DISGUSTED)

MIXY
(THE CONFUSED)

CANT
(THE FRUSTRATED)

BOOM
(THE ANGRY)

JUMPI
(THE SHOCKED)

BUBBA
(THE HAPPY)

DRAIN
(THE EXHAUSTED)

IMP
(THE MISCHIEVOUS)

Imp and the Fib Invasion

By Matt Casper and Ted Dorsey

Evergrow Ltd.

Hong Kong — Los Angeles

www.Emotes.com

ISBN 13: 978-988-17342-7-3

Printed in China

It was late at night in Emotia. Imp was working on his daily news blog, **The Emotia Times**. It was filled with all sorts of pictures and stories about what was happening in Emotia.

Imp was finishing an article on Super's win at the recent cyberhoops tournament. "I'm bored with writing the facts all the time," he said with a yawn.

Suddenly, Imp felt very playful. He had a very sneaky idea.
"HA! I just thought of a story that will really make my Emote friends
laugh!" Imp began typing quickly. "This is going to be *so* cool!"

The next morning began very peacefully in Emotia. The entire Internet was calm. But not for long.

One by one, the Emotes woke up. They were shocked by the news they read in *The Emotia Times*: **THE FIBS ARE COMING! THE INVASION OF EMOTIA IS UPON US!**

"The Fibs? What in the name of the Internet is a Fib?" muttered Mixy.

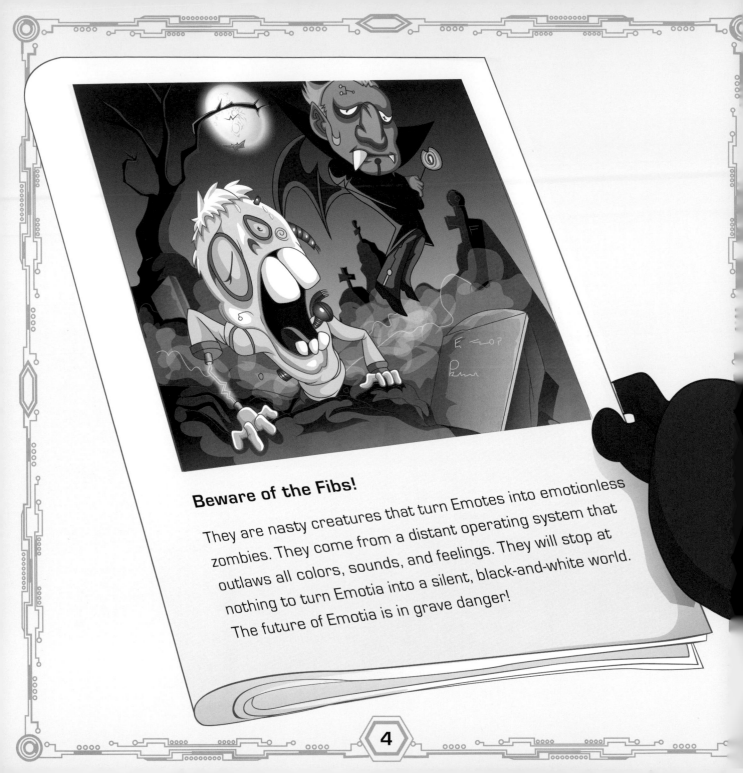

Beware of the Fibs!

They are nasty creatures that turn Emotes into emotionless zombies. They come from a distant operating system that outlaws all colors, sounds, and feelings. They will stop at nothing to turn Emotia into a silent, black-and-white world. The future of Emotia is in grave danger!

As the news spread of the Fib attack, the Emotes began to panic.

"I don't want to be a zombie!" shrieked Jumpi as he joined the other Emotes gathering in Emotia park.

Super addressed the crowd. "Listen up, everyone. We must be prepared! Boom, fire up the Emotablasters! Bubba, engage the Emoshield!"

Imp hid behind a cybertree and laughed. Then he snuck away to Macro's restaurant.

Imp found Macro standing behind the counter. "Hey, didn't you read the news today?" he asked.

"Nah, I never did trust **The Emotia Times**. You never know if they're telling the truth," Macro replied.

Imp frowned. He slurped down a fizzy pop and headed out the door.

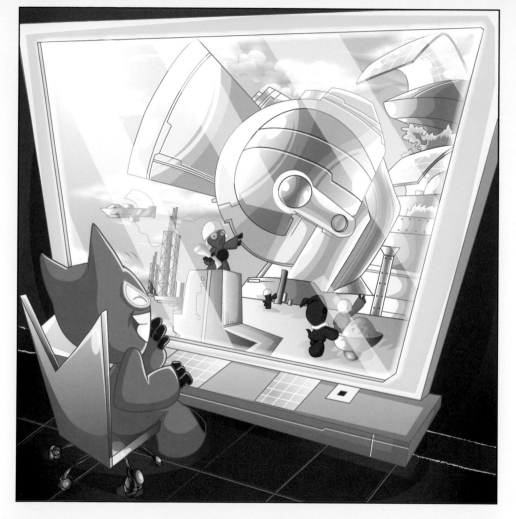

Imp logged on to the webcam for Emotia Park and saw Super preparing the Emotes for the Fib invasion.

"Priceless," laughed Imp.

Imp went to the website for Emotaspace and read a post from Cant. "I refuse to be silenced! Down with the Fibs!"

"Hilarious," laughed Imp.

"I've got to see this for myself!" thought Imp. He hid in the Zip Tube to watch as his mischief spread.

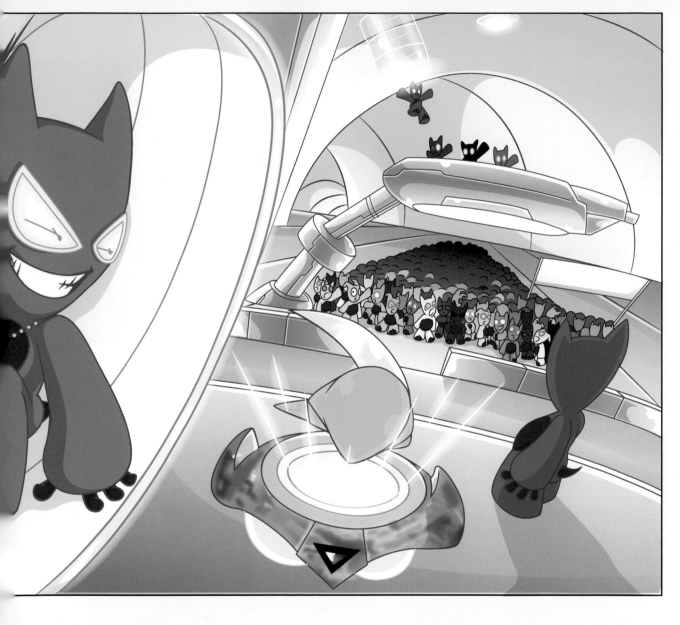

"This is the greatest joke in the history of Emotia!"

Feeling satisfied with his joke, Imp headed home. "I wonder what story I can make up for tomorrow's Emotia Times?" he thought.

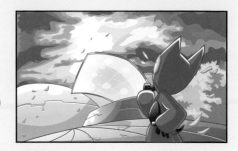

Imp's feeling of confidence soon turned into confusion.

"Where is everybody?" he wondered.

Suddenly, the digital sky began to grow dark. "Super? Boom? Where are you?" shouted a very frightened Imp.

With a flash, a giant flying disk appeared in the sky. It zoomed through the air then hovered silently above Imp's head.

The giant disk landed in front of Imp. A tiny door slid open and a group of very strange creatures emerged.

"Who are you?" shrieked Imp. The creatures didn't respond. They slowly started to surround Imp.

Imp realized that the creatures had no color. Their eyes were blank. In fact, they seemed to have no emotion at all. "FIBS!" screamed Imp.

Suddenly, a group of Emotes began to emerge silently and slowly from the shadows.

"THE FIBS!" Imp cried in horror.

The disk zoomed into the sky and began to whirl faster and faster. With a jolt, it shot a beam of laser light at Imp. It barely missed his feet.

Imp jumped into the air to avoid the blast. "Noooo!" he shouted in terror. He began to run away. The Fibs were right behind him.

The flying disk scanned everything in its path. It removed the colors from everything it touched.

Imp raced toward Emotia Gardens. All the pixel flowers had lost their color, and the streaming waters of the Emotafountain made no sound.

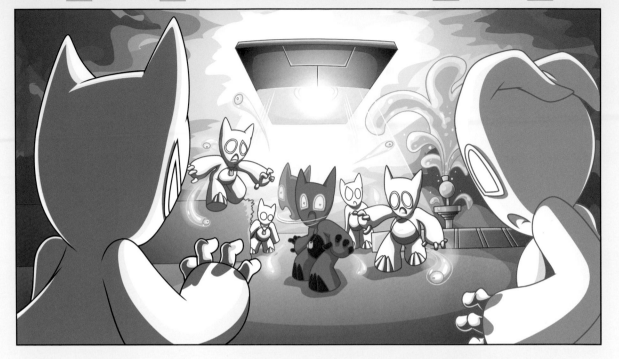

The Fibs came from all directions. They had him surrounded...
Imp was trapped!

"I guess this is it!" whimpered Imp. "Good-bye, feelings."

Imp closed his eyes and prepared to be zombified. For a moment, nothing happened. Then a soft voice began to speak.

"Imp, everything is going to be okay. You're safe."

Imp slowly opened his eyes. A-Net was hovering in front of him. His Emote friends were there too. Their color was restored, and they were smiling.

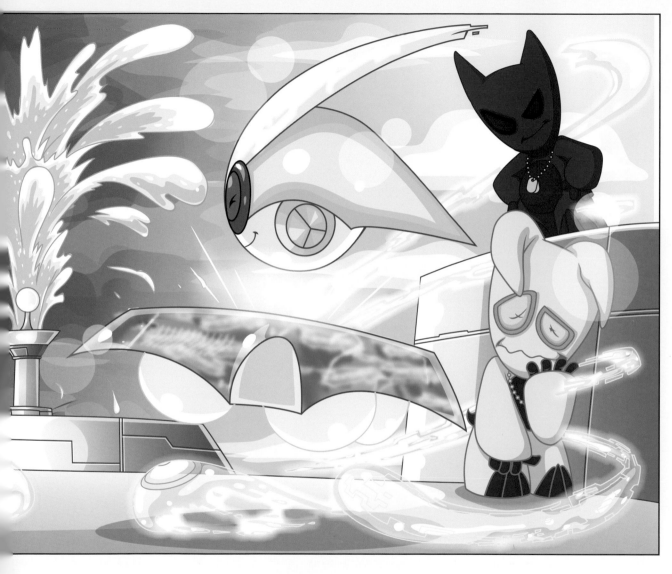

"What happened?" asked Imp. He was very confused.

"Gotcha!" laughed Super.

A-Net began to explain. "Imp, it's important to laugh and joke, but honesty is always the best policy. My simulotron created a virtual reality to show you how Fibs can cause a great deal of trouble."

"Sorry to trick you, but you had us all really freaked!" said Super.

Imp thought about how terrified he was when he'd thought the Fibs were real. "I guess I should have thought more about how my story would affect everyone's feelings," he said.

Super smiled. "Imp, we love your sense of humor! You make us laugh and you make Emotia fun. Just be careful to not go too far. Think before you joke!"

Imp thought about what Super had said. Then he did a backflip in the air and shouted, "TA-DA!" All the Emotes laughed and applauded.

Later that night, Imp sat at his e-pute. He wrote honestly about the day's events and reported all the facts of the story.

The next morning, when the Emotes woke up and logged on to their e-putes to check the news from **The Emotia Times**, they got a great big surprise. In big bold letters, the headline read, I'M SORRY.

Imp had told the truth.

THE END

About Practical Jokes

Having a sense of humor makes the world more colorful and fun. It's important to be able to laugh and enjoy the bright side of life. However, when you are not mindful of how a joke will affect the feelings of others, it can be very hurtful. Think about how your behavior might make someone feel. If you think that their feelings might be hurt, or that they could get all stressed out, STOP what you're doing!

When you don't tell the truth, you're in danger of running into a whole world of trouble. Do *you* like to be lied to? No? Guess what? No one does. Sometimes people lie to try to look cool or smart or special. But it just doesn't work. Nope. Getting caught in a lie makes you seem totally uncool. So be true to yourself. You are cool and smart and special just for being you!

◦◎ Don't forget to laugh. Laughing is very healthy. It will boost your mood and help you lighten up. So chill out and chuckle!

◦◎ Be aware of the effects of your behavior. Before you make a joke, ask yourself, "Will this hurt someone's feelings?" "Could this get me in trouble or put me in danger?" When in doubt, DON'T DO IT!

◦◎ Always say you're sorry. When you've hurt someone's feelings, it's important to apologize. It will make whomever you hurt feel better, and it will make YOU feel better, too.

◦◎ Be honest. Telling the truth is ALWAYS better than lying.

◦◎ It's okay not to have all the answers. Sometimes people lie when they don't know what to say. It's okay not to know everything. How could you? NO ONE does.

◦◎ You don't need to lie. Sometimes people lie because they want to look cool and want others to like them. That never works. Remember, you are special and cool just for being you!

Be True. Be Proud. Be You.

(Oh, and don't forget to laugh!)

ABOUT THE AUTHORS:

Matt Casper, M.A., MFT. Matt is a licensed Marriage and Family Therapist. He graduated from Duke University, where he studied psychology, religion, and film. He received his master's degree in Marriage and Family Therapy from the California Graduate Institute of Professional Psychology and Psychoanalysis. Matt currently lives in Los Angeles, where he works with people of all ages to help them identify, understand, and express their emotions.

Ted Dorsey is a writer and independent educator living in Los Angeles, California. A graduate of Princeton University, he has written for the stage, film, and television.

EMOTES!®

EMOTES! Abash and the Cyber-Bully
Matt Casper and Ted Dorsey

EMOTES! Cant Loses His Cool
Matt Casper and Ted Dorsey

EMOTES! Jumpi Goes to Camp
Matt Casper and Ted Dorsey

EMOTES! Drain and the Mystery of Sleep
Matt Casper and Ted Dorsey

Joi's Cybercoaster Adventure
Matt Casper and Ted Dorsey

EMOTES! Super and Perfecto
Matt Casper and Ted Dorsey

EMOTES! Imp and the Fib Invasion
Matt Casper and Ted Dorsey

EMOTES! Ick and the Emotastone
Matt Casper and Ted Dorsey

Yawni and the Perspecto-Goggles
Matt Casper and Ted Dorsey

Boom the Anger Tamer
Matt Casper and Ted Dorsey

Bubba Under Pressure
Matt Casper and Ted Dorsey

EMOTES! Mixy's Quest
Matt Casper and Ted Dorsey

AND MANY MORE!

Reading is fun and makes you really smart!